O Come, All Ye Faithful

Peg Augustine

Illustrated by Patricia Ludlow

Abingdon Press
Nashville

O Come, All Ye Faithful

ISBN 978-0-687-64304-2

07 08 09 10 11 12 13 14 15 16—10 9 8 7 6 5 4 3 2 1

Printed in China

A word from the author:

While based on facts, this book is a work of fiction. Little is known about John Francis Wade, and we have nothing that tells us what he was thinking and feeling when he wrote O COME, ALL YE FAITHFUL. Still, we cannot sing this beloved hymn without feeling the depth of awe and love that flowed from his heart. The words and art in this story combine in an invitation to us to join the heavenly chorus in singing praises to the newborn king.

Likewise, we do not know everything that Mary and Joseph were thinking as they waited for the birth of God's Son. The Bible leaves no doubt, however, that they were both faithful people of God who willingly accepted their part in bringing about that first and best Christmas gift—Jesus Christ, the promise of our salvation fulfilled.

For more on the history of John Francis Wade and O COME, ALL YE FAITHFUL, see the notes at the end of the book.

Peg Augustine

O come, all ye faithful, joyful and triumphant,
O come ye, O come ye, to Bethlehem.
Come and behold him, born the King of angels;
O come, let us adore him, O come, let us adore him,
O come, let us adore him, Christ the Lord.

True God of true God, Light from Light Eternal,
lo, he shuns not the Virgin's womb;
Son of the Father, begotten, not created;
O come, let us adore him, O come, let us adore him,
O come, let us adore him, Christ the Lord.

See how the shepherds, summoned to his cradle,
leaving their flocks, draw nigh to gaze;
we too will thither bend our joyful footsteps;
O come, let us adore him, O come, let us adore him,
O come, let us adore him, Christ the Lord.

In the sixth month the angel Gabriel was sent by God to a town in Galilee called Nazareth, to a virgin engaged to a man whose name was Joseph, of the house of David. The virgin's name was Mary. And he came to her and said, "Greetings, favored one! The Lord is with you." But she was much perplexed by his words and pondered what sort of greeting this might be. The angel said to her, "Do not be afraid, Mary, for you have found favor with God. And now, you will conceive in your womb and bear a son, and you will name him Jesus. He will be great, and will be called the Son of the Most High, and the Lord God will give to him the throne of his ancestor David. He will reign over the house of Jacob forever, and of his kingdom there will be no end." Mary said to the angel, "How can this be, since I am a virgin?" The angel said to her, "The Holy Spirit will come upon you, and the power of the Most High will overshadow you; therefore the child to be born will be holy; he will be called Son of God.". . . Then Mary said, "Here am I, the servant of the Lord; let it be with me according to your word."

Luke 1:26-35, 38a

Now the birth of Jesus the Messiah took place in this way. When his mother Mary had been engaged to Joseph, but before they lived together, she was found to be with child from the Holy Spirit. Her husband Joseph, being a righteous man and unwilling to expose her to public disgrace, planned to dismiss her quietly. But just when he had resolved to do this, an angel of the Lord appeared to him in a dream and said, "Joseph, son of David, do not be afraid to take Mary as your wife, for the child conceived in her is from the Holy Spirit. She will bear a son, and you are to name him Jesus, for he will save his people from their sins." . . . When Joseph awoke from sleep, he did as the angel of the Lord commanded him.

Matthew 1:18-21, 24a

John Francis Wade stood looking out his window deep in thought. Christmas was fast approaching and he felt sad. He missed his home in England. Outside his window, the River Scarpe flowed peacefully by. In the distance he could hear the bells from the Hotel de Ville. John saw people beginning to hurry toward the Church of Notre-Dame.

He knew that a crèche would have been set up in the cathedral and that faithful parishioners would soon be bringing gifts to leave at the Christ Child's cradle. His thoughts turned to the faithful couple who had made the journey to Bethlehem that first Christmas so long ago.

In those days a decree went out from Emperor
Augustus that all the world should be registered.
This was the first registration and was taken while
Quirinius was governor of Syria. All went to their
own towns to be registered.

Joseph also went from the town of Nazareth in Galilee to Judea,
to the city of David called Bethlehem, because he was descended
from the house and family of David.

Luke 2:1-4

When the herald announced the decree

from Caesar Augustus, Mary and Joseph were not sure what to do. Joseph would have to travel to Bethlehem, but Mary's baby would soon be born. Should she make the trip or stay at home? Finally they decided she should go along, and they set off in the company of their relatives. Mary rode on their gentle donkey and Joseph walked by her side.

The miles that divided Bethlehem from

Nazareth seemed a long, long way indeed. It would take at least three days to reach their destination.

During the day the travelers walked as much as they could, stopping only for short breaks to refresh themselves with water and to let their animals rest. At noon they ate a meal of raisin cakes, olives, and goat cheese. When it became too dark to walk safely, they built campfires, ate another simple meal, wrapped themselves in their tunics, and slept as well as they could on the hard ground. How Joseph wished there was extra water so that Mary could wash the dust from her feet.

At last the journey was almost over.
In the distance, Joseph could see the little huddle of buildings that was Bethlehem. He smiled up at Mary as he stroked the donkey's velvety nose.

"Soon you will be able to get some real rest," he said. "We'll find a nice room and you can lie down on a soft rug. We'll buy some bread and fish in the marketplace, and perhaps there will be fresh cucumbers as well."

But Joseph was a little worried. The closer they got to town, the more crowded the road became with people and animals. As soon as they entered Bethlehem, he began stopping and knocking on doors, looking for a place Mary could rest for the night.

But all the guest rooms were filled. As much as they wanted to help, even Joseph's friends could not find space for another person to sleep. Finally a kind innkeeper offered them a place to sleep in his stable, where the animals spent the night.

Turning from his window, John Francis
Wade surveyed his cozy room. Though small, it was filled with books and manuscripts. Clearly it was a place where one who loved words and music could be happy.

His thoughts still on the throngs filling the streets of Bethlehem so long ago, John picked up a pen and began to write in Latin: *Adeste, fideles, laeti triumphantes.*

Scooping sweet-smelling hay into a bed for Mary, Joseph gave thanks to God for a safe end to their journey, for the shelter of the stable, and for the warmth the animals there gave to them.

That night Jesus was born. Mary held
him close and smiled down at him. As she brushed the
cloud of dark hair away from his tiny face, she marveled
that God's Son should be asleep in her arms.

Centuries later and many miles away,

John Francis Wade was filled with the same sense of awe. Compared to a little house in Bethlehem, his room was a palace. To think that the King of angels was born in a rude stable, wrapped in bands of cloth, and laid down for his first night on earth in the box where the animals fed! *Natum videte, Regem angelorum,* he wrote—behold the King of angels! *Venite adoremus, Dominum*—Come, let us adore the Lord!

Wade's heart soared along with the melody he created. He thought of how Jesus, truly God since before the beginning of time, loved humankind so much that he came to earth to be born and to live as a humble carpenter and traveling rabbi. *Deum de Deo*—God of God. *Lumen de Lumine*—Light of Light.

In that region there were shepherds living in the fields, keeping watch over their flock by night.

Luke 2:8

In Palestine there are only a few months in the year when the rains make pasture lands hospitable for sheep. On the night that Jesus was born, a group of shepherds had been taking full advantage of the abundant grasses. During the day each shepherd had led his flock to a different section of pasture, but when night fell they gathered together for company and for safety. The flocks mingled together in a fold built years ago by the shepherds' ancestors.

Once they were ready to sleep, one of the shepherds would lie down in the opening to the fold both to keep the sheep in and to keep out wild animals and thieves. Now though, they gathered around a campfire, stretching sore muscles and reveling in the warmth of the fire. Looking up into the starry sky, one of them began telling a story that was almost as old as the world itself. When he had finished, another took up his flute and began playing a tune that had come to him just that day.

As the notes from the song died away,

the shepherds became aware that
the night sky was becoming almost
as light as day. They shifted uneasily,
looking around to see what could be
causing this phenomenon. Suddenly in
the light they saw a figure. Now they were
terrified. But as soon as the angel began to
speak, their fear left them. The shepherds were simple men
of the earth and their work often kept them from participating
in the religious activities at the Temple. But they knew God's
promise of salvation for God's people.

And suddenly there was with the angel
a multitude of the heavenly host, praising God and saying,
    "Glory to God in the highest heaven,
    and on earth peace among those whom he favors!"

When the angels had left them and gone into heaven, the
shepherds said to one another, "Let us go now to Bethlehem and
see this thing that has taken place, which the Lord has made
known to us." So they went with haste and found Mary and
Joseph, and the child lying in the manger. When they saw this,
they made known what had been told them about this child; and
all who heard it were amazed at what the shepherds told them.

                                                        Luke 2:13-18

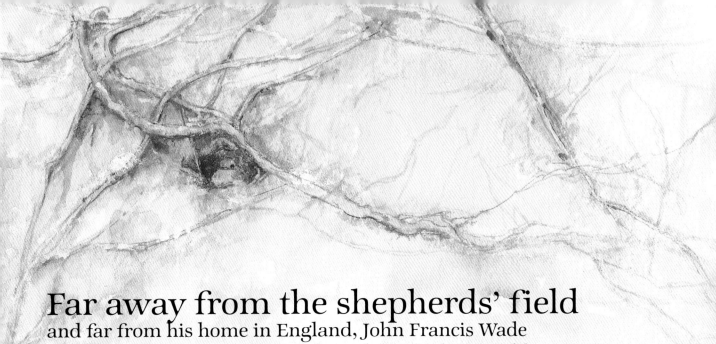

Far away from the shepherds' field

and far from his home in England, John Francis Wade continued to work on the words and music that would centuries later become one of the most beloved Christmas carols. There were no better words than those sung by the angel choir—Glory to God, all glory in the highest! Gloria in excelsis Deo!

Wade's heart was touched as he thought of how these humble men had not hesitated even one minute, but had hurried to the baby's side. Centuries had passed since that night, but the faithful still joyfully left everything to adore the one who came to earth as the Savior, the Messiah, the Lord.

En grege relicto, humiles ad cunas,
Vocati pastores approperant;
Et nos ovanti gradu festinemus.

See how the shepherds, summoned to his cradle,
leaving their flocks, draw nigh to gaze;
we too will thither bend our joyful footsteps;

Today the faithful continue on a journey,

Bethlehem is still a town that many long to see, and everyone can "bend their joyful footsteps" to love the child who loved us so dearly.

On Christmas Eve and Christmas morning, churches are filled with people singing triumphantly,

Yea, Lord, we greet thee,
born this happy morning,
Jesus, to thee be
all glory given.
Word of the Father,
now in flesh appearing:

O come, let us adore him, Christ the Lord.

Adeste, fideles, laeti triumphantes;
Venite, venite in Bethlehem.
Natum videte Regem angelorum.

Refrain
Venite adoremus, venite adoremus,
Venite adoremus, Dominum.

Historical Notes

John Francis Wade was a Catholic composer who fell victim to the Jacobite rebellion. Escaping to France, he joined the Roman Catholic College and Ministry Center in Douay, France. While teaching music at the college, he also wrote music and copied both his compositions and the musical scores of others by hand. His manuscripts were works of art and people prized them as much for their beauty as for the music.

For some time scholars believed that Adeste Fideles was merely an old Latin Christmas carol that Wade had copied, but today most acknowledge that Wade composed both the lyrics and the music. Seven manuscripts of the song have been found in his handwriting and bearing his signature. The earliest is from 1751 and can be seen at Stonyhurst College, Blackburn, England.

Frederick Oakeley translated the carol into English. His first attempt was while he was the pastor of Margaret Street Chapel, and began "Ye faithful, approach ye." Years later he changed his translation to read, "O come, all ye faithful, joyful and triumphant!"

The final verse beginning, "Yea, Lord we greet thee," is usually sung only on Christmas Eve or Christmas morning. An unknown writer added the verse beginning "Lo, star-led chieftains," to commemorate the wise men and extend the carol's use to Epiphany.

Yea, Lord, we greet thee,
born this happy morning,
Jesus, to thee be
all glory given.
Word of the Father,
now in flesh appearing:

**O come, let us adore him,
Christ the Lord.**

Please Return To
Dr. Lisa Waites